Speaking, Listening and Drama

John Airs and Chris Ball

CONTENTS

YEAR ONE, TERM ONE
Going on a bear hunt 5
- Listening and responding to complete stories and poems
- Drama activities – improvisation
- Speaking for different audiences – describing incidents from their own experience
- Discussion and group interaction – investigating, selecting, sorting

YEAR ONE, TERM TWO
Keeping safe 12
- Discussion and group interaction – planning, predicting, exploring
- Drama activities – performance and improvisation
- Speaking for different audiences – retelling and telling stories
- Listening and responding to instructions from the teacher

YEAR ONE, TERM THREE
Hercules 17
- Listening and responding to taped stories or video
- Discussion and group interaction – explaining, reporting, evaluating
- Drama activities – responding to drama
- Speaking for different audiences – reading a story aloud

YEAR TWO, TERM ONE
Holidays 23
- Discussion and group interaction – investigating, selecting, sorting
- Speaking for different audiences – reading notices and dialogue aloud
- Listening and responding to others in the class
- Drama activities – responding to drama

YEAR TWO, TERM TWO
The Pied Piper 29
- Drama activities – responding to drama
- Discussion and group interaction – planning, predicting, exploring
- Listening and responding – watching others' presentations
- Speaking for different audiences – telling real and imagined stories

YEAR TWO, TERM THREE
Looking after pets 35
- Listening and responding – to a talk by an adult
- Drama activities – performance
- Discussion and group interaction – explaining, reporting, evaluating
- Speaking for different audiences – presentation: explaining processes or information

PHOTOCOPIABLE RESOURCE SHEETS 40

Published by Hopscotch Educational Publishing Ltd,
29 Waterloo Place, Leamington Spa CV32 5LA
(Tel: 01926 744227)

© 2002 Hopscotch Educational Publishing

Written by John Airs and Chris Ball
Series design by Blade Communications
Illustrated by Cathy Gilligan
Cover illustration by Sue Woollatt
Printed by Clintplan, Southam

ISBN 1-902239-96-2

John Airs and Chris Ball hereby assert their moral right to be identified as the authors of this work in accordance with the Copyright, Designs and Patents Act, 1988.

Those responsible for the introduction of the literacy hour to primary schools stated very clearly that speaking and listening was to be at the heart of literacy. Easily said, but is it so easily done? In an attempt to reaffirm the importance of speaking and listening the QCA produced *Teaching Speaking and Listening in Key Stages 1 and 2* in 1999 (Ref QCA/99/391).

The 'Framework for planning' in this document, while quite prescriptive, is not overly descriptive and leaves much to the imagination. In principle that is an excellent thing, but in practice finding time to flesh out the bare bones of someone else's plans can simply become another burden.

The three books in this series offer practical examples of the fleshed out framework. Organising and managing speaking and listening in the classroom calls for careful planning, which takes time. We hope that the series of lessons in these books will provide ideas for such planning.

The importance of drama

Drama is one of the first art forms that children experiment with. From the earliest age they act out imagined situations and put themselves, sometimes literally, in other people's shoes. By the time they come to school they are often very good at it.

Speaking and listening, reading and writing, studying almost any area of the curriculum, can be enhanced by setting the work within a fictional or dramatic context. Meeting a bear in its cave can add to the fun of reading about it. Playing Red Riding Hood's mother may help a child understand something of a mother's viewpoint and concerns.

And classroom drama does not have to be high drama. Many of the drama elements in these lessons are low key affairs. What children find intriguing is working in role and, sometimes at least, working with their teacher in role.

None of this calls for highly trained acting skills. In role you are simply representing someone in an imagined situation. You can make mistakes, plead ignorance, be quite incompetent, because you are not being you. You are representing someone else. It is acceptable, indeed it is good, to ask the children what you should say and do in role. You are giving them responsibility and making things easier for yourself.

Using themes

The National Curriculum has, in some cases, tended to reduce teaching to a set of unconnected activities. What these books attempt to do is to recover the connections. There is a thematic core to each of the sets of lessons and, while focusing on the objectives for speaking and listening as outlined in the QCA framework, we try to link them to reading and writing and to other areas of the curriculum, not as disparate exercises but within a unified context.

We have called each set of objectives as laid out in the framework Lessons One, Two, Three and Four but each lesson may take more than one period of a school day.

Finally, it is worth saying that these lessons have been tried and tested in various classrooms and children do seem to enjoy them.

About this book

This book is organised into six chapters, one each for each term of Years One and Two. Each chapter is on a theme, such as 'Keeping safe', so that the children can be working on the same topic throughout the term while addressing different aspects of the Speaking, Listening and Drama curriculum in each lesson.

The chapters

Within each chapter there are four lesson plans. These address the following aspects of the subject (although not always in the same order):

- Speaking for different audiences
- Listening and responding
- Discussion and group interaction
- Drama activities

The lesson plans

The majority of lesson plans are organised into the familiar literacy hour format of:

- Whole-class activity
- Group activities
- Plenary session

There may be one or two occasions where the nature of the activities has dictated that the lesson plan move away from this rigid format, but it has been planned in such a way that the lesson can still be completed in the time allocated for the lesson.

Each chapter has the following guidance:

Overall Aims

This itemises the aims of all four lessons and relates more to the topic being addressed than the Speaking, listening and drama objectives.

Resources

This is a list of the resources that teachers might need to help them deliver the objectives of the

lessons in that chapter. These include the photocopiable sheets, which are optional, as teachers may wish to supply their own resources.

Each lesson plan has the following guidance:

Intended learning

These are taken directly from the QCA's guide, *Teaching speaking and listening in Key stages 1 and 2*. For the most part the lesson plan includes all of the objectives from the guide but where it was felt the lesson would become too unwieldy not all of them are addressed.

Some lesson plans have the following guidance:

Notes for the teacher

This might be background information to the topic being addressed or suggestions for extension activities.

Photocopiable sheets

Speaking, listening and drama are not activities that normally lend themselves to the use of photocopiable activity sheets. However, there are some sheets included for some of the lessons. These aim to help the teacher explain the content of the lessons or aid with recording and other aspects of the lessons.

Going on a bear hunt

Overall aims

- To respond imaginatively as a whole group to an illustrated story, reading the pictures as well as the written text.
- To explore how a story can be told from different points of view.
- To consider the consequences of one's actions.

Resources

- Copies of *We're Going on a Bear Hunt* by Michael Rosen and Helen Oxenbury (Walker Books, 1993). If you don't have a copy of this particular book your class can still undertake the activities in this chapter. You will just need to tell them the story first.

  Note: If you have a copy of the book, Helen Oxenbury's illustrations reveal the various moods, reactions and interactions of the family. For this book in particular, reading the pictures is as important as reading the text.

- Large sheets of paper, including A1 size.
- Felt-tipped pens.
- Pictures of clothing, food, camping equipment and raw fish.

In this first lesson the children are introduced to the first part of the story and think about the different parts of the family's journey to find a bear. They respond to the story by using gestures to describe the different movements and then by drawing pictures of the different parts of the journey. Finally they show their pictures and say the onomatopeic words from the story.

Lesson One
Listening and responding
(to complete stories and poems)

Intended learning

- To sustain concentration.
- To participate appropriately.
- To reinforce the meaning of verbs and prepositions through actions.

Whole class

✳ Enjoy a whole class reading of the first half of *We're Going on a Bear Hunt* up to the point where they enter the cave (the page with 'WHAT'S THAT?' in the book).

✳ Discuss with the children the variety of intonation required: enthusiasm for the expedition, joy at the beauty of the day, bravado (false bravado?) on 'We're not scared', then apprehension when the obstacles are confronted. Ask 'How are we going to say each line? If we make our voices louder and louder, what effect does that have?'

Swishy swashy!
Swishy swashy!
Swishy swashy!

'Are we being a little frightened at first, then getting bolder and bolder as the experience starts to become fun? Or is it getting more and more scary for some of the characters?'

✳ Say to the children 'Let's read that part of the story again but this time let's add some gestures. What would be suitable?' For 'We're going on a bear hunt,' they could scan the horizon; for 'We're going to catch a big one,' they could reach as high as possible; then arms wide to welcome the beautiful day; and a thump on the chest or hands on hips to show not being scared. Then being scared! What might that look like?

✳ Finally, mime the prepositions, over, under and through when they occur.

Groups

✳ Organise the children into groups and give each group one of the parts of the story to illustrate:

- swishy swashy through the grass
- splash splosh through the river
- squelch squelch through the mud
- stumble trip through the forest
- hoooo woooo through the snowstorm
- tiptoe tiptoe through the cave

Plenary

✳ Invite the groups, in the order of the story, to stand up and show their pictures and say the onomatopeic words. You may need to help them with this.

✳ Then, as a class, chorus the six sounds or actions, swishy swashy, splash splosh, and so on, so that the children are beginning to learn them by heart in preparation for Lesson Two.

✳ Finish with a second reading, incorporating all that has been rehearsed, again stopping as they tiptoe through the cave.

✳ If most of the children do not already know this book, it would be appropriate at this point to ask what they think the family might find in the depths of the cave and what might happen next. Ask anyone who has read the book before to keep the ending a secret at this moment so that the others can predict freely.

Lesson Two
Drama activities
(improvisation)

In this second lesson the children revisit the first part of the story, then investigate the characters in the story and how these characters feel, so that they can act out the different roles. They then listen to the rest of the story and act out the return of the family to their home, with some of the chidren being the family and others being the materials the family has to pass through.

Intended learning
- To explore familiar themes and characters.
- To respond to 'teacher-in-role' to explore character.
- To respond in role to create stories.

Whole class
✻ Ask the children to remind you of the first part of the story. Make sure they use the terminology from the story: 'We're going on a bear hunt', 'swishy, swoshy' and so on.

✻ Choose six children to represent the characters in the story: Dad, the four children and the dog. Tell the rest of the class that they will have their chance to be an actor later.

✻ As you read the story again, let the group act out the first part of the story until they enter the cave. They tiptoe through the cave till…

✻ Stop at this point and explain that the actors must 'freeze' just where they are when you read 'WHAT'S THAT?'

✻ Ask the six children representing the family members to stand exactly as they are in the picture. Ask the other children to come up in turn and say what one of the characters (including the dog) is feeling. Ask 'How do you know? What clues in the picture tell you this?' (If you don't have a copy of the book, ask the children to imagine how the different characters might feel. Is Dad brave? Is the dog frightened or brave?)

✻ Read the part of the story where we see that in the cave is a BEAR! The 'THAT' in 'WHAT'S THAT' will, in fact, be you, the bear, hunched at the far end of the long cave. Become the bear as you read, hunched over and staring at the family. The children who are the family will no doubt react!

✻ After everyone has calmed down, read the remainder of the story together. Go back through all the different scenes heading for home and point out how the bear is always following and getting closer and closer but never quite catching up.

Groups

❊ Organise the children into groups: one to be the family (a different group of children this time) and six to be the different scenes the family has to pass through to get home: the cave, the snowstorm, the forest, the mud, the river and the grass.

❊ As you go round the groups advising, they should discuss how they will best portray their role:

- Should the group being the cave hold hands over the heads of the family?

- How can the group acting as the snow behave? Would darting fingers give the impression of driving snow?

- How will the trees in the forest stand?

- Should the children crouch down as big blobs of mud?

- How could they make themselves into water for the family to pass through?

- Is there enough space between the wavy blades of grass for the family to go through? Can they remember the sounds of the grass?

Plenary

❊ Let the class act out the end of the story.

❊ Finally, ask the class to study the picture of the bear padding off, back to its cave. Ask, 'What is the bear thinking and feeling right now?'

❊ In role as the bear again, hunch your shoulders a little to suggest the disconsolate looking animal we see in the picture; explain how you feel as you lumber off across the moonlit sands alone. You may adopt the suggestions the children have just made or challenge them with your own ideas of the bear's thoughts and feelings. You had been hoping to make some new friends perhaps or you wanted to find out why these strangers were creeping into your home. Are you tired of being hunted maybe?

Lesson Three
Speaking for different audiences
(describing incidents from their own experience)

In this third lesson the children retell the story, remembering the events and the order in which they happened. They retell the story in the roles of the different characters in the story. They then consider their own lives – times when they have been happy or afraid and what happened.

Intended learning
- To sequence events.
- To show some awareness of the listener.

Whole class

✳ Ask the children to tell you the story again. Choose different children to tell you different parts of the story. Remind them to tell the story in the correct sequence and to use the same repetitive language: 'We're going on a bear hunt' and 'swishy, swashy'.

✳ Say 'Now – they said they would not go on a bear hunt again, but they never stopped talking about this one. How do you think each of them might have told her or his story?' Tell them that you are going to organise them into pairs so that they can discuss how to tell the story from a different character's point of view. You will need to give them some examples:

- Tell the story from the point of view of Dad. 'Well, we decided it was such a lovely day that we would go off and have an adventure. We discussed what we wanted to do and we all agreed that we would go on a bear hunt. So off we set. Well, the first thing we came to was a field of very tall grass…' and so on.

- You could tell the story from the point of view of the big sister. 'Well, they all decided they wanted to go off on an adventure but I didn't want to go. There was a good cartoon on the telly and I wanted to watch it. But my little sister kept tugging at my hand…'

✳ Talk about how the different versions of the same incident vary.

In pairs

✳ Organise the children into pairs and let them decide whose story they want to tell. Try to pair more confident speakers with less confident ones to avoid causing any distress – not everyone enjoys being a public speaker!

Return to whole class

✳ After they have spent five minutes discussing which character they want to be and how they feel about the story, choose some of the children to tell their versions. Ask 'Who chose to be the little sister?' or 'Who chose to be the dog?' Make sure you listen to as many different versions as possible.

✳ Discuss why some of the class said what they did (evidence in the text or illustrations?) and how effectively they felt they told their part of the story. What principles of storytelling might be emerging from this exercise? (Establishing the scene, the occasion and the characters; describing events clearly and in planned sequence; selecting relevant detail; incorporating elements of contrast, conflict, surprise, tension, relief; working to a climax and resolution.)

✳ Now say 'Has anyone been on a journey when they were frightened?' If you feel this approach might cause distress say 'Has anyone been on a journey when they were very happy?' The aim is to get the children talking about their own experiences and how they felt.

Plenary

✳ Put on a different persona and tell the children that you are the mother of the family that went on the bear hunt. Say something like, 'Right, now I want to know exactly what happened this afternoon. I have just seen the state of the clothes you left in the bedroom! And look at that dog! What have you been up to? I shall be back in a moment to hear what you have to say.'

✳ Choose some children to tell you the story again. Remind them that this time they are not telling it as if it was an adventure but explaining what they had done and why they don't want to get into trouble! They will have to add details for you to see the events in your mind's eye. Ask for such details if they are missing. How deep was the water? How cold? They will also have to think how an irate mum and wife will respond to the story they are telling. They will be showing awareness of the listener and responding in role to their teacher in role. Have as much fun with this situation as you can!

Lesson Four
Discussion and group interaction
(investigating, selecting, sorting)

In this lesson the children plan an expedition to visit the bear – not to hunt it. They have to plan the journey, working in groups to sort the equipment they will need.

Intended learning
- To devise ways of sorting items.
- To ask and answer questions.
- To make relevant contributions.

Whole class
✳ In role as Mum again, ask the family (the whole class on this occasion) if they would like to go, not on a bear hunt, but a bear visit. Tell the children that they will return to the bear's cave but to visit, not hunt, the bear. Discuss what might be the difference. Explain that this time they will be properly prepared.

✳ Ask the children what they need to prepare for the visit. For example, planning:

  - clothing
  - food
  - other supplies
  - a map
  - how to approach the bear and show that they want to be friends.

✳ Consider the questions involved in these tasks. For example:

  - What particular items of clothing should they bring if at least part of the route is as before?
  - What will the weather be like? Should they take sandwiches and cold drinks or flasks of soup?
  - Will they need equipment, such as ropes, to help them?
  - Might there be alternatives to fording the river? On their map, could there be a bridge near enough for them to cross the deep, cold river?

- Might there be an alternative path above the stretch of thick oozy mud, which last time they thought they couldn't go round?
- Should they come bearing gifts for the bear? If so, what would be suitable?

Groups
✳ Organise the children into groups of six to represent the family including the dog. Tell them that each group is to take responsibility for a specific task. (If, as is likely, your class does not divide exactly by six, spread the extra children around the complete groups.) There are five tasks mentioned above. If there are fewer than five 'families', coalesce two or more of the tasks. Give each group a large sheet of paper and some felt-tipped pens and set them to work.

✳ You and any assistants can help the children. You are asking them to devise ways of sorting items. The group responsible for sorting the clothes needs to consider:

- What clothing would be suitable for snow? (They could either draw the list of clothes or you could appoint or act as a scribe.)
- What do we need for the river?

and so on.

Another group needs to consider:

- What food would be suitable for a sunny day?

- How will we keep it cool?

and so on.

❊ Other points that might be considered are:

- Who could carry what?

- What risks might we face?

- Should the dog be on a lead as we enter the cave?

- Should the dog enter the cave at all?

- Should a small advance party approach the bear first?

❊ Encourage the children to ask the appropriate questions themselves and to make relevant contributions to the planning. The challenge is to listen to each other and negotiate an agreed list, map, or mode of approach to the bear.

❊ If some of these tasks appear too demanding for your children, an alternative approach to selecting and sorting items might be to provide pictures of items of outdoor clothing, different footwear, picnic food, rucksacks, camping equipment, a large raw fish for the bear. Ask the groups to select the items they would require for their particular task from the assortment of pictures.

Plenary

❊ Invite each group to report on its plans, which you (as Mum) and the others will now discuss together and agree. Again encourage questions. Ask, 'Are we trying to carry too much now? Will this journey take longer and will we have to stop and make camp?'

❊ Say to the class, 'Right, it's time to go. Have you got everything?' Make a rapid check, allowing for imaginary preparations among the whole group. 'Have you got the compass there? Where's the map? Let's just check where we're going first. Good. Let's go.'

❊ With the class gathered round you, make as if to set off on the journey, with the children carrying whatever they have selected. Then stop and ask the class to sit down just where they are. Then say, 'And this is the story they told of their bear visit ... So what happened?'

❊ Encourage as many children as is feasible to contribute to the telling. Narrate the stages of the journey up to and including what might happen when they finally visit the bear. After hearing a number of no doubt contradictory accounts, try to agree on a satisfactory conclusion, one that seems to satisfy most of the class.

❊ You could now summarise the children's story on the board or on sheets of A1 paper to create a class big book called 'We're Going on a Bear Visit'.

Have you got everything?

Keeping safe

Overall aims

- To identify and reflect on issues of safety as understood by this age group.
- To explore these issues as advisers to Little Red Riding Hood, a notable risk taker.
- To practise and reflect on elements of dramatic storytelling.

Resources

- A piece of red cloth, the size of a child's coat, to be used as a cloak.

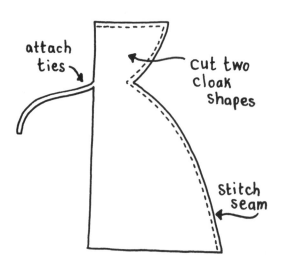

- Five or six sticky notes with a sketch of a red cloak.
- Photocopiable Sheets One and Two (pages 40 and 41).

In this first lesson the children are introduced to safety situations involving the well-known character, Little Red Riding Hood. They consider ways in which she puts herself in danger, then discuss a plan to help her be safe.

Lesson One
Discussion and group interaction
(planning, predicting, exploring)

Intended learning

- To take turns to speak.
- To listen to others' suggestions.
- To talk about what they are going to do.
- To recall what is already known about keeping safe.
- To discover the essentials of safety at this age.

Whole class

✳ Remind the children of the story of Little Red Riding Hood and how, in spite of being warned not to, she left the path through the woods to pick some flowers and was seen by a wolf who would not have seen her if she had stayed on the path. Ask the children what happened to Little Red Riding Hood after that.

✳ Say to the children, 'Well, I've been talking to Little Red Riding Hood's mummy and she says she is getting quite worried about her. She says she's a good girl but sometimes she just doesn't think carefully enough about keeping safe. The other day she went for a walk in the park with her mummy and little brother. She had an argument with her brother and she ran away and hid from them both. They searched everywhere for her – calling "Little Red Riding Hood, Little Red Riding Hood!" – but all they could find was her red cloak dangling from the branch of a tree.'

✳ Here, hold up the cloak and mime unhooking it from an imaginary branch. Call out Little Red Riding Hood's name as if you are looking for her. Tell the children that they searched everywhere for her and it was getting dark when at last they found her, curled up asleep under a big thick bush.

✳ Ask the children if they can understand why Little Red Riding Hood's mummy was worried about her. What might have happened to her?

✳ Then tell the children another tale of woe. 'The other day Little Red Riding Hood saw an ice cream van outside school. She rushed away from her mummy and ran right between two parked cars and across the road. "Little Red Riding Hood! Stop! Stop!" Her mummy grabbed after her but all she was left with was her coat.'

✳ At this point, produce the red 'cloak' again and mime snatching it in mid-air as if you were the mother grabbing at Little Red Riding Hood.

✳ Tell the children that luckily there was nothing coming so Little Red Riding Hood was alright, but her mummy was very upset.

✳ Discuss why her mummy was upset – what might have happened to Little Red Riding Hood?

Groups

✳ Tell the children that, in order to keep Little Red Riding Hood safe, they are going to help her by planning her route to school. Arrange the class into mixed working groups and give the children copies of the picture of the road outside Little Red Riding Hood's school (Sheet One page 40). Point to the house where she lives (with the arrow) and then tell them that they must discuss together, listen to each other and then agree the route from her house to school.

✳ Also give each group sticky notes, each with a red cloak drawn on it. Encourage the groups to discuss safe ways of crossing a road like the one in the picture and to decide where Little Red Riding Hood should cross. Ask them to place the sticky notes in places that are suitable for crossing the road.

Plenary

✳ Invite each group to share their plans for Little Red Riding Hood's route to school. Enlarge the picture on an OHP or whiteboard and agree a good route. Use sticky notes to mark the place where the children agreed it would be safe to cross.

✳ Talk about how the children come to school. What routes do they take? Do they have to cross any roads? Are they aware of how dangerous it can be?

Lesson Two
Drama activities
(performance and improvisation)

In this second lesson the children are asked to take on the roles of Little Red Riding Hood, her mother and brother and to investigate how those characters felt about Little Red Riding Hood being in danger. They consider and explain how they would feel themselves if they were in that situation. Finally, they discuss how their actions can affect other people.

Intended learning

- Act out own stories and other well-known stories to different audiences.
- To respond as themselves in a fictional setting to create a story.
- To understand how one's actions affect others.

Whole class

✳ Briefly remind the children of the story of Little Red Riding Hood hiding in the bushes after the argument with her brother (from Lesson One, page 12). Use the red cloak as a symbol of the missing child, as in Lesson One.

✳ Ask for a volunteer to represent Little Red Riding Hood's mother. Invite them to the front and ask them to hold the red cloak as though they have just unhooked it from the tree.

✳ Encourage the other children to make suggestions about what Little Red Riding Hood's mother is thinking. Then ask the children to form a circle around the child who is playing the mother and invite some children, one at a time, to approach her from behind and to voice her thoughts at this moment.

I'm worried about Little Red Riding Hood-she doesn't stop to think...

✳ Ask the child who has been representing the mother to sum up what she is thinking and feeling.

✳ Say to the children 'Do you think Little Red Riding Hood knew what her mother was feeling?' Encourage them to consider and discuss how important it is to consider the effect of our actions on others.

✳ Invite another volunteer to represent Little Red Riding Hood's brother. Say 'Imagine you are Little Red Riding Hood's brother. How do you feel about what has happened?'

✳ Find another volunteer to represent Little Red Riding Hood herself. Put the cloak round this child's shoulders. Tell the children that they are going to recreate the moment when the cloak became snagged on the tree. Someone could act as the branch on which the cloak is snagged and the other children form the tangle of bushes under which Little Red Riding Hood crawls to hide.

✳ When the children are in position, direct the mother and brother to call for her. Indicate that the others should be silent. After a brief pause, ask the class what they think Little Red Riding Hood is thinking. She could give her own thoughts from the 'bush'.

✳ Remind the children that eventually Little Red Riding Hood grew tired and, in the darkness, beneath the thick leaves of the big bush, she fell asleep. Some time later she was woken up by her little brother who had finally found her hiding place.

Plenary

✳ Discuss how Little Red Riding Hood might have felt when she woke up. Ask them to put themselves in her place. How would they have felt? Would they feel guilty about the worry they had caused the mother and brother?

✳ Draw conclusions about how important it is to realise how our actions can affect others.

Lesson Three
Speaking for different audiences
(retelling and telling stories)

In this lesson the children as a class retell one of the two different stories about Little Red Riding Hood and then work in groups to plan and tell another story.

Intended learning

- To order events using story language.
- To include details to help the listener.
- To speak clearly.

Whole class

✳ Tell the children that you want them to think about how we tell stories. You want them to learn how to tell stories to other people. Briefly remind them of the two stories about Little Red Riding Hood putting herself in danger and worrying her mother.

✳ Choose one of them and together plan how to tell it to, for example, another class. Ask the children how they would start the story. Aim for the response 'Once upon a time…' Write this on the board.

✳ Now ask 'What was the first thing that happened in the story?' Aim for the children to tell one of the stories to you, giving details. If, for example, someone says 'Little Red Riding Hood and her mother and brother were walking in the park', say 'When was this? What time of day? What time of year? What was the weather like? Describe the park.' Make notes on the board as you agree the story line and the details.

✳ Talk about the following (using language the children can understand):

- clarity – the importance of speaking clearly so that the people who are listening can hear every word of the story.

- pace – when should we use slow speech and when should our voices get faster?

- variety of tone – should we use the same tone all the time? Demonstrate some examples. Say 'I was so frightened' in a dull, boring voice. Ask the children 'Is this how you would say it when you are telling a story?'

- gesture – should we use our hands and arms when telling a story?

There was a huge troll...

✳ Go on to complete the story together, making notes on the board as you go.

✳ Finally, ask someone to volunteer to tell the whole story, using your notes on the board and help from the others. Does anyone else want to tell it as well?

✳ Tell the children they are now going to work in groups to plan out another story and to practise it ready to tell it to other people.

Groups

✳ Give the children copies of photocopiable Sheet Two (page 41). This contains the story in cartoon format of Goldilocks and the Three Bears. The groups have to use this picture story to practise telling it to other people.

✳ Go round the groups as they are planning, reminding them about using different tones of voice and gestures.

✳ Tell them they can each tell a part of the story if they prefer. They should practise their parts carefully. Remind them that they have to speak clearly so that the people who are listening will be able to hear.

Plenary

✳ Invite the children to tell their stories. They could either tell these to the other groups or to an invited audience, such as another class.

✳ After everyone has told their stories, discuss the different ways that were used to tell the story. Did anyone speak clearly? Did anyone use pace, variety of tone or gestures? Did they enjoy the storytelling session?

Lesson Four
Listening and responding
(to instructions from the teacher)

In this lesson the children consider different dangers that a child might face. They tell a new story about Little Red Riding Hood and how she should avoid a particular danger.

Intended learning
- To follow instructions accurately.
- To ask for clarification if necessary.

Whole class
✳ Hold up the red cloak so that all the children can see it. Tell them that you have just found this cloak in the playground. There was no sign of Little Red Riding Hood, though. What do the children think she may have got up to this time?

✳ Encourage responses. The focus here is to identify dangers so that the children can think of how to avoid them. Although the intention is to encourage the children to think of incidents that could put a child of their age at risk, you don't want to frighten them or fill them with gloom. If, therefore, they suggest fanciful or unlikely ideas, it may be advisable to go along with them, at least for a time, even if the results are comic. The point of setting these lessons within the Little Red Riding Hood framework is to explore serious matters within the safety of dramatic fiction.

✳ List on the board the possible dangers the children suggest that Little Red Riding Hood may meet this time. Draw their attention to others you consider significant if they have missed them.

✳ Choose one of the dangers to be developed into a story. Discuss what might have happened.
- What time of day was it?
- What was Little Red Riding Hood doing in the playground at the beginning of the story?
- Who else was there?
- What did she do that was dangerous?
- How did she lose her cloak?
- Where is she now?
- What happened in the end?

✳ When you have agreed your new story about Little Red Riding Hood, tell the children they are now going to work in groups to discuss the topic of safety.

Groups
✳ Organise the children into small groups. Tell them you want them to talk and agree about four things. Write them on the board.

1. What was Little Red Riding Hood doing that was dangerous?

2. What should she do to stay safe in the story setting?

3. Where is one place in our school playground that could be dangerous?

4. How could we make sure we are safe when we play there?

✳ Tell the children they will be asked to report back to the class with their answers. Make sure they understand what they are required to do by asking them in turn to say what the four things are that they need to discuss.

Plenary
✳ Ask the groups to each choose a spokesperson and report back to the class on the group's findings.

✳ Did they manage to follow all the instructions?

✳ Did they have to ask for any clarification? If they did, tell them this is good because it is important when we have to follow instructions that we have understood those instructions before going off and doing the wrong thing!

Hercules

Overall Aims

- To think about the qualities and characteristics of a hero.
- To analyse and reflect on the ways that the media represent and sell heroes and their images.

Resources

- 'Hercules' video (Disney).
- Large sheets of paper.
- Felt-tipped pens.
- Pictures of celebrities such as Rambo/Terminator/David and Victoria Beckham.
- Music: 'The Planets' Suite' by Holst.
- A flip chart.
- Photocopiable Sheets Three, Four and Five (pages 42 to 44).

In this lesson the children watch part of the Hercules video, making notes as they do so about what they like and don't like about the extract. They then work in groups, using the notes, to discuss each other's points of view. Finally, they come together as a class for a debate on the extract.

Lesson One
Listening and responding
(to taped stories or video)

Intended learning

- To express views about how the story has been presented.
- To compare others' views of the tape or video.

Whole class

✳ Before the lesson, the children should have seen the complete 'Hercules' video. Summarise the plot.

'The story takes place in ancient times in the far away land of Greece. Hercules, the mighty hero, has been charged with performing twelve supreme tasks or labours by King Eurystheus, who is jealous of his strength and power. He travels the world to accomplish them and, in spite of their extreme difficulty, he ultimately succeeds.

'The Disney cartoon, which is the focus for this exploration of the story, is based on the original myth but in this video version, Hercules has a trainer called Philoctetes who promises to help and support him in his tasks. Philoctetes is a satyr, a mythical creature who is half man, half goat. He will make money for himself if Hercules triumphs and proves himself a hero.'

✳ Show the children the excerpt where Hercules has a battle with the hydra, a terrifying snake-like creature, whose heads regrow several-fold when they are chopped off, and the subsequent marketing of Hercules as a hero (the song). This is approximately 42 minutes into the video. Start from where Hercules says, 'Phil, I did great. They even applauded…'

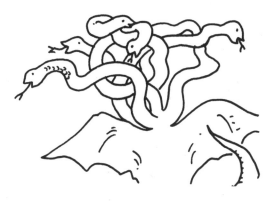

✳ Tell the children they are going to watch the excerpt again but this time they will be watching it in order to make an appraisal and to analyse it critically. For example, they might note:

- the dramatic effect of the music;

- the speed of events as the heads of the hydra multiply – to the point where it is almost a blur;

- the humour of the moment when the hydra belches after he has swallowed Hercules;

- the dreadful quiet of the crowd when Hercules is crushed under the rocks with the hydra;

- the huge cheers when Hercules rises from the clenched claws of the dead hydra.

(You will need to have previewed the relevant section of video prior to the lesson.) Give out copies of photocopiable Sheet Three (page 42) which contains two columns for comments – one for things they like and the other for things they don't like. They should use this to record their thoughts as it will help them to remember and be focused in their criticism, by referring to specific moments from the film, when they go into their pair and group discussions.

Pairs and groups

✳ Organise the children into pairs and ask them to talk to their partners about their most and least favourite parts of the video extract. This will give them practice in speaking and listening skills in a pair before they use these skills in a larger group.

✳ Then organise the children into larger groups. Discuss their reactions to the video with them and, if necessary, help them explain the reasons for their choices. Talk about how some of the children's favourite moments are other children's least favourite parts of the video.

✳ If you have a classroom assistant, the children could be split into smaller groups, with the teacher or assistant prompting them and helping them articulate their ideas in more detail.

Plenary

✳ Record the children's ideas and opinions on a large sheet of paper. You could use the same format as photocopiable Sheet Three (page 42). The sheet can be used as a reference and reminder of the range of their opinions in the class.

✳ After the children have aired their views, you could suggest a critical tennis match between those who liked and those who disliked the episode. Sit in a central position and adopt the role of the film's director. Seat your advocates on one side and your detractors on the other.

✳ Tell the children to take turns in bombarding you from each side with their opinions. Encourage them to give reasons for their point of view. Remind them to use appropriate tones of voice, for example friendly voices for praise and more hostile voices for criticism. Ask the children to articulate how you, as director, might feel at the centre of this critical storm.

✳ You could also set up a circle time activity where the children talk about another film or book they liked and why they liked it. Do not force children to participate. They can just say 'pass' if they have no instant ideas. Children who pass can offer their ideas later if they wish.

Lesson Two
Discussion and group interaction
(explaining, reporting, evaluating)

In this lesson the children consider the way in which Hercules is portrayed in the video and then go on to look at what constitutes a hero. They work in groups, explaining their ideas to each other. Finally, they agree what to say and elect a spokesperson to present their views to the class.

Intended learning

- To explain views to others in the group.
- To choose a spokesperson for the group.
- To organise group views to be presented to the class.
- To consider the issues around the concept of celebrity.

Whole class

✳ Tell the children that they are going to discuss the way Hercules is characterised in the film.

✳ To do this, use the 'Role on the wall' strategy. Start with a large drawn outline of Hercules (you could use the one on photocopiable Sheet Four (page 43) enlarged or on an OHP or whiteboard). Write 'Hercules' at the top. Layers of description of Hercules will be built up inside and outside the outline until a rounded and detailed picture emerges.

✳ Talk about the way that Hercules is presented in the video. Ask the children for ideas. For example, at the start of the video he is not as muscular as later on but he is strong but clumsy. Later he is shown as muscular, good looking and kind. At this stage, don't talk about what a hero is; just concentrate on how Hercules is presented.

✳ How is music used in the video? Is it different when Hercules is appearing? What sort of music is used to present him when he defeats the hydra (dramatic)?

✳ Then invite the children to say what they think Hercules is like. Write these ideas inside the outline figure. For example, at the start of the story before he becomes a hero he is 'strong', 'clumsy', 'kind', 'helpful' and 'caring'. During the extract he is 'huge', 'very strong', 'proud', 'happy' and so on.

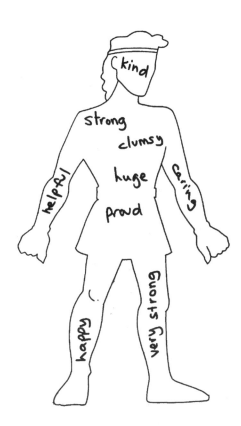

✳ As the character takes shape, reinforce and clarify particular children's ideas with the whole class where you feel it is appropriate. Pin up the outline as a reference point for all the class to look at. It can be added to as new layers of character are suggested.

✳ Now introduce to the children the word 'hero'. Can anyone tell you what it means? Can anyone think of a hero – fictional or factual? Start them off with some ideas, such as the woodcutter who saved Little Red Riding Hood or a man who rescues someone from a freezing river. Tell the children they are now to work in groups to discuss heroes.

Groups

❊ In groups, the children should discuss the actions and qualities a hero demonstrates. They should then write or draw their ideas on blank paper or they could use photocopiable Sheet Four (page 43). For example, a child could draw Hercules fighting the hydra and underneath label it 'bravery' (with your or the classroom assistant's support).

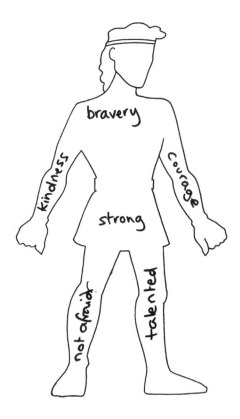

❊ They should discuss each other's ideas and agree a list of descriptions for a hero.

❊ Finally, they should appoint a spokesperson to tell the rest of the class what they have agreed.

Plenary

❊ Have a time of feedback from the groups about the qualities of a hero. You could introduce the idea that the children are speakers and listeners at a meeting at which people can only speak when they hold a symbol that allows them to address the meeting. Make or find something suitable, such as a walking stick, to use (a listening staff). When this is held by the speaker, it demands attention and concentration from everyone.

❊ All the actions and qualities mentioned by the children should be noted on a large sheet of paper, which can complement the 'Role on the Wall' outline from the beginning of the lesson.

❊ After all the children's ideas have been presented, show pictures of heroes (for example, male and female pop, sports stars or a child who battles against a heart defect or leukaemia), from magazines, newspapers, or the Internet. Ask the children if these stars meet their criteria for heroism. If any new criteria are identified as a result, add them to the list in a different coloured pen.

❊ As a whole group, discuss what things people did in the film to turn an ordinary man into a famous hero. Play two pieces of music – 'Mars' and 'Jupiter' from 'The Planets' Suite'. Discuss the different rhythms and feelings that each evokes and ask the children which piece of music would best accompany the hero as he does heroic things. Ask the children to justify their choice.

Lesson Three
Drama activities
(responding to drama)

In this lesson the children consider the way in which Hercules is marketed and then choose and plan a freeze frame drama of one of the ways to present to the class.

Intended learning

- To consider motives and issues in response to others' performances.
- To consider character, motive and story development by reflecting on drama.
- To think critically and analytically about the concept of celebrity.

Whole class

❋ In front of the children, act out the role of a Hercules who cannot cope with fame. Say, 'I know that I should be happy. Wherever I go people recognise me and say nice things to me. They want my autograph. They smile and say, "Hello". I see my picture in the shops, in books and magazines, and in McDonald's they have little figures of me. All these things are happening around me…'

❋ Out of role, tell the children that they are going to show some of the things that people do to sell Hercules so that he can see them happening around him. Ask them if they can remember ways in which Hercules could be 'sold', for example:

- T-shirts with an 'H' on
- Greek vases with pictures of Hercules on
- a statue
- credit cards with Hercules' name on
- a Hercules action-type toy
- Hercules sandals
- Hercules drinks
- a Hercules theme park
- Hercules' handprints in concrete like the Hollywood film stars

❋ Discuss and agree the strategies and note them on the board for all to see. If the children need prompting, show the song from the video where Hercules is marketed (see Lesson One, page 17).

Groups

❋ Organise the children into groups, then explain to them that you want them to create a still picture, or freeze frame, of a way in which to sell Hercules.

❋ Show them exactly what to do by choosing some children to model an example. For example Philoctetes, as Hercules' trainer, might get a photographer to take a picture of Hercules so that children can put up a poster of him in their bedrooms. Set up this idea as a still image or freeze frame with a child as the photographer and another child as the hero. Ask them to hold their positions so that everyone can see clearly what is happening.

❋ Assign to groups particular ideas from the list you have just made with the whole class. As the groups work on their ideas, circulate to offer help and advice. When the children have planned and made their still images in groups, invite everyone to come together to show their work.

❋ Ask the watching children to point out moments from the performance that they liked and say why they liked them. They can then suggest improvements or changes to less impressive moments and ask questions of the performers about their intentions, where necessary.

Plenary

❋ Decide who will go first and assign a number to each group. As you say their number, each group should come forward slowly and create their image. This creates a sense of performance and anticipation as the images gradually and formally take shape. You can then say, 'The picture fades', at which point the children return, again in slow motion, to their places, ready for the next group's image to emerge.

❋ As they perform, the rest of the class should describe what they are doing. For example, 'Philoctetes arranges for a sculptor to make a giant sculpture of the hero…'

❋ Talk about how other people are marketed, such as famous footballers. Are they heroes?

Lesson Four
Speaking for different audiences
(reading a story aloud)

In this lesson the children practise reading the story of Hercules and then read it aloud to their peers.

Intended learning
- To read with some variety in pace and emphasis.
- To comment on how reading relates to features of punctuation marks and layout.
- To prepare a storytelling for an audience.

Whole class
✳ Explain to the children that, in their previous lesson, they made up, acted out and told part of a story. Say that now you want them to retell the whole story aloud.

✳ Agree what the story of Hercules is. Enlarge a copy of photocopiable Sheet Five (page 44) on an OHP or whiteboard. Read it through with the children. Make sure you use the punctuation to guide how you tell the story. For example, when you read 'the Fates – three horrid females!' pause after the dash so that the next three words are crystal clear. Where exclamation marks are used, change the tone of your voice. For example, for 'But during the fighting Meg is accidentally killed!' your voice should perhaps be raised.

✳ Tell the children that they are going to work in groups to record the story in their own way. Remind them that they will need to make the story sound really interesting so that the people who listen to the story will concentrate on what is said.

✳ Talk about the happy and sad moments of the story. For example, Hercules is happy when he defeats the hydra and the people call him a hero but he is sad when Zeus tells him he cannot be a god. Ask some children to demonstrate what a sad or happy voice sounds like so that they will know how to tell the story in the appropriate way when they come to sad and happy moments.

Groups
✳ Organise the children into their groups to record their story and then to practise ways of telling it, saying the words in such a way as to make the story interesting for the listener. (If necessary, they can use the story on photocopiable Sheet Five.) They should practise saying the words to each other and then together so that they can speak them chorally.

✳ If any of the children are using the story on page 44 you could work with them to underline the happy and sad parts in different colours so that they are prepared to change their voice as they read.

Plenary
✳ Let some of the children read their stories. When individuals or groups say their emotional words, encourage the rest of the class to repeat them with the same emphasis so that they are echoing the words AND the way they are said.

✳ Talk about the differences between the narrative and the feeling passages. Discuss the need for appropriate pace and variety in their reading.

✳ You could arrange for the children to read their story to another class, or to parents, children and teachers in an assembly.

Holidays

Overall Aims

- To think about what is involved in going on a journey.
- To consider the roles and responsibilities of passengers and airport employees.
- To think about what we need when we reach our destination.

Resources

- Artefacts such as cups, saucers, plates (for café), books, magazines (for a paper shop) – as appropriate for airport locations.
- A digital camera.
- Large sheets of paper.
- A map of the world or Europe.
- Amplification equipment.
- A sample passport and/or tickets.

Before starting this series of lessons, check that a substantial proportion of the class has travelled by air. When we have previously worked on this topic, at least 80 per cent of children have travelled by air at this age. It is not a major problem if several do not have that experience. They can easily empathise with the protagonist played by the teacher in role for whom this will be the first flight. Many of the activities around the theme arise from the anticipation and anxieties involved in any sort of journey.

> In this lesson the children discuss different possible holiday destinations, agree one to go to, discuss what the airport might be like and then, in groups, decide what they are going to take on holiday with them.

Lesson One
Discussion and group interaction
(investigating, selecting, sorting)

Intended learning

- To listen to each other's views and preferences.
- To agree the next steps to take.
- To identify contributions from each group member.

Whole class

✽ Tell the children that you are all going to decide on a place to visit for the holidays. Take various suggestions from them and check where they are on a map, making sure that the whole group can see where the possible holiday locations are and how far they are from home.

✽ Ask the children what they enjoyed on previous holidays and whether they would go there again. List the most popular holiday destinations, suggested then have a vote on where to go.

✽ Next, talk about how you are going to get there. Contrive the discussion so that it is agreed that you are going to have to fly! Ask how many of the children have been in an aeroplane. Can they remember what it was like? Can they remember what the airport was like? Talk about the following points about an airport:

- The automatic doors – what sound do they make? Why are they automatic? (So people don't have to struggle with suitcases?)

- The check-in desk – was there a queue? Was anybody in the queue anxious about missing a flight? How can you tell when someone is anxious?

- Going to the departure area – did they have to put things on a conveyor belt for the X-ray machine? Why do they think this has to be done?

- The departure lounge – what was this like? Noisy? Lots of people? Could they see planes out of the window? Was there somewhere to have something to eat and drink? Were there shops?

✵ Now tell the children that they must decide what to take on holiday. Model the small group activity with the whole group by drawing a suitcase on the board. Ask what would be appropriate to take on holiday. Challenge the children's suggestions if necessary. For example, would you take a coat to Egypt in summer? Write their suggestions in the suitcase shape.

✵ Talk about the different needs and interests of children and adults. What do adults enjoy about a holiday? What do children enjoy about a holiday? This will influence the choice of baggage items.

Groups

✵ Organise the children into groups. Give each group a large sheet of paper. Ask them to discuss and then draw the contents of their 'suitcases' for their holiday in your chosen location. The best working arrangement is for one child to draw or write everyone's suggestions, with this role rotating around the group. Make sure that no one person dictates the contents of the suitcase. They must all listen to each other's views and then agree on a choice.

✵ Circulate round the groups to help them label items and ensure that everyone has the opportunity to scribe. Finally, tell the children to put their names and addresses on the corners of their cases.

Plenary

✵ When the task is completed, let each group feed back an item from their 'suitcase' to the plenary. There should only be one of each item. You can write up the items on the board to create a collective class case. This is a good activity for ensuring that the children listen to others' ideas.

✵ Introduce a new tension to the preparation. Tell the children that their bags are packed and that they are waiting for the taxi that will take them to the airport. Remind them of their previous discussions about the airport.

• How do they feel?

• What are their worries?

• What expectations do they have of the holiday?

• Have they forgotten anything?

✵ Scribe these feelings around an outline of a person's head.

Lesson Two
Speaking for different audiences
(reading notices and dialogue aloud)

In this lesson the children consider the different roles of the people who work at the airport. They work in groups to develop the roles of these different people, ready to make a spoken presentation to the class in role.

Intended learning
- To convey rhythm.
- To speak with clarity and use intonation.
- To compare differences in presentation.
- To bring the airport to life.

Whole class
✣ Tell the children that they are going to imagine they are at the airport. Remind them of the discussions about an airport that they had in Lesson One. Which different areas are there in the airport?

- The check-in desk
- The entrance to the departure area
- Passport control
- The departure lounge
- The shops
- The restaurants or cafés
- The gate

✣ Talk about the different people they will meet at each of these different parts of the airport. If they have been to an airport what were these people like? What did they say?

- The check-in desk: why is this person here? To check your tickets and passport, give you a boarding pass, check in your luggage and tell you where to go next. How do they speak? They ask questions, such as 'Did you pack your bag yourself?' and 'How many bags do you have?' You can ask them questions, such as 'Please may I have a window seat?' and 'Is the plane on time?'

- The entrance to the departure area: is anyone here in uniform? Why? You have to put your things on the conveyor belt. You might put your money and watch in a tray. Why? You have to walk through an arch that detects whether or not you have anything metal on you. What happens if the alarm sounds as you walk through? How does the person in uniform speak to you? What does he or she do?

- Passport control – who is here? Do they speak? What are they wearing?

- The departure lounge – who is there? What are they doing? Are they all passengers waiting for their planes? Is anyone anxious?

- The shops – who is there? Is it serve yourself so there is only someone on the checkout? What do they say? What do you say?

- The restaurant or café – who is there? What do they say? 'Can I help you?' What do you say? 'Please may I have a breakfast and a cup of tea.' What about behind the scenes?

- The gate – finally, you are about to board the plane. Who is there? What are they wearing? What do they say? Are they smiling and welcoming?

✣ Tell the children they are going to work in groups to take the parts of the people they have been discussing. They must make sure they speak in the way those people would, taking care to understand who they are talking to and what is the correct way to talk to those people.

Groups

✽ Organise the children into groups and give each group a role to play.

✽ One group could suggest particular things that happen in a café and give examples of what might be said, for example the cooks cut up food in the kitchen, the counter assistant serves the passengers or waiters/waitresses carry trays. When they have worked on this, ask them to discuss and decide together one question that their group might ask (for example, waiters – 'What can I get you, Madam?').

✽ Another group might consider how the check-in clerk might deal with angry or late passengers. They should discuss and write down questions that the children think the clerk might ask and how they could ask them. Would they be pleasant and patient all the time?

✽ Other groups should consider the roles of the other workers at the airport as discussed. They should agree one or two questions to ask in role ready to present at the plenary session. They should be very aware of how each different character speaks. It is important that the groups agree on questions, rather than statements, as these will be used in the next lesson.

Plenary

✽ Ask the children to take turns to present their airport workers and speak their lines.

✽ Agree that each of them spoke in a different way because each of them was dealing with a different situation. The way in which you might speak to an angry passenger who is late will be different from the way in which the person at passport control will speak to you if you can't find your passport and you look suspicious!

✽ When everyone is quiet, suddenly make a tannoy announcement (using amplification if possible) for a flight and destination. Make it unclear. Produce a sheet of paper with the words of the announcement on it. For example: 'Passengers on flight 123 for Corfu are requested to proceed to the check-in desk as soon as possible.'

✽ Ask the children how this announcement should be said. Let some of them try out the announcement for clarity and tone. Have fun as individual children try out their own indecipherable announcements! Challenge the other children to work them out. Compare the differences in presentation.

Lesson Three
Listening and responding
(to others in the class)

In this lesson the children re-enact their roles from Lesson Two and present their questions, this time so that the other children can respond to them – again in role.

Intended learning

- To ask relevant questions.
- To follow instructions – for example, in a pair or a group.

Whole class

❋ Remind the children of the different workers at the airport as discussed in Lesson Two. Tell them to imagine that they are now arriving at the airport. Narrate the arrival at the automatic doors. Use sound effects to enhance the effectiveness of their actions.

❋ Describe the arrival of the traveller. For example, 'As the doors hiss and clunk open, you look around, seeing the cafés, bustling with waiters and customers examining their menus and eating, the shops with books and magazines, where families buy things to read on their journeys. You hear crying babies, children arguing and parents anxiously staring at the departure boards and you feel…'

❋ Encourage the children to discuss how the nervous traveller stands, walks and speaks. Incorporate their thoughts into the unfolding narrative. They should listen carefully as contributions are made by individuals.

❋ Tell the groups' spokespersons from Lesson Two that they are going to ask aloud again the questions they agreed upon in that lesson – this time because the passengers (individual children) will be giving a response. Starting with the check-in clerk, let the 'workers' ask their questions. This time another child in the class, in role as a passenger, should answer that question. Don't have this session prepared, as the children's spontaneous reactions to the questions can be very interesting and lead to discussions later.

❋ Carry on until all questions have been asked and answered.

Groups

❋ In different groups from Lesson Two, let the children work to create further brief snatches of dialogue from the workers at the airport.

❋ Circulate to suggest and reinforce ideas.

Plenary

❋ Arrange the groups so that they are spread about the room. Ask them to stand still while they wait for you to narrate them into action. Bring each group into action briefly, one at a time, as if you are a camera focusing on activities and short conversations. This is an exercise in listening, concentrating and appraising work.

❋ Bring the class together and ask them to say what they liked about the ideas they heard and saw. They can also suggest ways that the groups could improve and redraft their ideas.

❋ This is all in preparation for Lesson Four in which the whole thing will be brought together for a class drama.

❋ You may like to challenge more able children by coming into their areas in role as, for example, a difficult customer. They will have to respond instantly to problems. For example, in the café, you could be a customer complaining that the soup is cold and asking the café's staff what they are going to do about it. Or in the shop, you could be a customer who has lost her child and doesn't know what to do about it. Take ideas from the children about how the workers should respond to these emergencies and difficulties.

Lesson Four
Drama activities
(responding to drama)

This lesson sees the culmination of the previous three lessons, in which the whole class enacts a drama about going on holiday by plane, which involves a detailed look at an airport and the people who work there.

Intended learning
- To adopt appropriate roles in small or large groups.
- To use texts, materials, artefacts, images and objects as stimuli.

Whole class
✳ Discuss the different activities in the previous three lessons:

- Where it was agreed to go on holiday, what the airport would be like and what to pack.

- What the roles of the different workers at the airport are and what they say as part of their jobs.

- How people might respond to the questions put to them by the airport workers.

✳ Tell the children that all this will be put together into a drama. Adopt the role of an inexperienced traveller, and say, 'I'm going on holiday. It's my first time by plane, so I don't know what to do. I wonder if you could help me?'

✳ Set up still pictures of the different areas in the airport with the children playing the roles they did in Lesson Two. You may need a large area to do this. Each part of the airport should be featured, from the automatic doors to the final gate.

✳ Use as many of the available materials and equipment as you can for the different areas. For example, you could use bodies for the automatic doors, a table for the check-in desk, bodies for the X-ray arch, a table for the conveyor belt and so on.

✳ Set the scenes carefully, letting the children direct where possible. In the café, have the waiters and counter assistants together with customers at a table. Use artefacts such as trays, cups and plates, to help the children focus on the activities.

✳ Once every scene and actor is agreed, ask everyone to get into place. As you go around the room to the different areas, narrate your journey: 'The new passenger walked slowly round the airport, watching and listening carefully to what was going on. He watched the actions of the different groups of people and he listened to their conversations. First, he passed through the automatic doors ... then he went to the check-in desk. While he was waiting in the queue he noticed the café and the workers providing food for hungry passengers...' Carry on in this vein until you have visited every area and have heard their dialogues.

Plenary
✳ Ask everyone to sit down somewhere where they can see you. Discuss the performance. What was good? What wasn't so good? How could it be improved?

✳ If you are happy with the performance, do it again with another traveller and then put on the whole show for another class or the parents!

The Pied Piper

Overall Aims

- To consider the consequences of breaking promises and telling lies.
- To dramatise and analyse a traditional poem.
- To create a set, costumes and characters within an historical setting.

Resources

- 'The Pied Piper' poem by Robert Browning, preferably an illustrated version such as that by Kate Greenaway. There is also a version on the Internet.
- Pictures of a medieval town.
- Hans Holbein's picture of Henry VIII and Brueghel's picture of children playing, 'Children's games'.
- Music (Vivaldi,'s 'Four Seasons', Holst's 'The Planets' Suite' and Debussy's 'Prélude a l'aprés-midi d' un faune').
- Photocopiable Sheets Six, Seven and Eight (pages 45 to 47).

In this first lesson some of the children should be helped to set up an atmospheric scene depicting the town of Hamelin and its town hall. The other children will watch as the scene is set and consider the setting, its mood and atmosphere.

Lesson One
Drama activities
(responding to drama)

Intended learning

- To consider aspects of stagecraft in a live or recorded performance.
- To consider other elements of performance that create mood and atmosphere.
- To create the setting and atmosphere of a scene.

Whole class

✻ Show the children some pictures of a medieval town (for example, Chester or York with their narrow streets and half timber houses) or display the picture on page 45. Then show them pictures of wealthy burghers (Holbein's Henry VIII would suffice), such as that on page 46. Seeing this will help the children to be aware of the setting and period of time of the poem.

✻ Read the opening lines of Browning's poem:

'Hamelin town's in Brunswick by famous Hanover city. The River Weser deep and wide washes its walls on the southern side.'

✻ Explain that Hamelin has grown rich by developing its trade with other places.

✳ Tell the children that some of them are going to create a theatre set of the town and place in that set the politicians. Others will take on the roles of the politicians. (You will need to let at least half of the class become the audience as the purpose of this lesson is for them to respond to the set.)

✳ Hamelin's town hall will also reflect the status and importance of the town's politicians. Explain to the children that it is their responsibility as councillors to decorate the town hall to the highest quality. Discuss and note what the main chamber of Hamelin town hall might look like. Ideas might include gold-framed paintings of hunts, sculptures, fine tables and chairs and lavish cutlery and china. Draw and write the children's ideas on the board. This will be the first draft of their design.

Groups

✳ Now, referring to the plan the children have created, let the children work in groups to create the set, using their own bodies to form the furniture and the paraphernalia of the council chamber. Physical theatre is an exciting form used by many theatre groups. In this lesson it is used to create a real, three-dimensional sense of space and atmosphere. For example, the children could create a large table, statues, pictures, stained glass windows and an imagined town crest.

✳ One of the groups should take on the roles of elected politicians in Hamelin, such as the wealthy burgher shown in the picture. Talk about the significance of the dress the politicians would wear – fur, jewels and lace.

✳ Play bustling, busy music (such as the opening movement of Spring from Vivaldi's 'Four Seasons') to accompany the set that the class has created. Take a photograph of the 'set' and use it as a springboard to writing.

Plenary

✳ As the set takes shape, those who are watching can describe in detail the artefacts that have been created in the classroom space. For example, the legs of the table are intricately carved from the finest oak and the stained glass shows goods being unloaded at Hamelin docks.

✳ Ask the audience to describe the atmosphere of the set. How could it be improved?

✳ How did the music affect the mood?

Notes for the teacher

As an extension activity, the class could write a speech of welcome for an honoured guest to be received at the town hall.

Lesson Two
Discussion and group interaction
(planning, predicting, exploring)

In this second lesson the children are going to work together in groups to create still images of the rats and the different places in which they were to be found. They should work as a team, discussing who undertakes what, considering all the alternatives and reaching an agreement before putting on their final presentation.

Intended learning
- To ensure everyone contributes.
- To allocate tasks.
- To consider alternatives and reach agreement.

Whole class
✳ Play some ominous music such as Holst's 'Saturn'. Discuss with the children the possible sounds and sights of the scene at Hamelin quayside at midnight. Write their ideas on a board or flip chart. For example:
- Dark.
- The water slurps against the sides of ships and the moon glistens on its surface.
- A ship bobs on the water.

✳ Focus on a particular ship that is tied up. Tie a rope between some chairs or tables. If you are in the hall you could tie it between a high wall bar and a chair. Then narrate: 'As the honoured guest arrived down the gangplank of his grand ship, full of rich goods for the people of the town, down ropes and chains at dead of night, other guests secretly left the ship – rats!'

✳ A sock over your hand can effectively 'creep' down the rope and convey the mood of the moment and the movement of the rats.

✳ This will now bring you to the poem itself. Read the second stanza of the poem.

'Rats!
They fought the dogs, and killed the cats…'

Groups
✳ Tell the children that they are going to work in groups to create a still image of one of Browning's descriptions of the rats. Model this for them by choosing one of the actions of the rats and creating a still image. This will enable them to see how the image is formed gradually, with one person at a time adding to the picture. Invite different children to play the roles of different characters in the image or to make the shapes of different objects (such as a cradle for the baby to lie in).

✳ When you have modelled this, give each group a particular action and ask them to work together to create still images. Working together should involve:

- everyone agreeing who is to play the part of the rats
- allocating tasks to members of the group
- appointing a spokesperson, if neccesary
- appointing a director, if necessary
- considering all the alternatives for such an image
- agreeing on the final presentation

✳ If they decide they would like to speak the stanza chorally as they set up their images, help them with this.

Plenary
✳ Bring the children together to present their still images. Suggest to the groups that, before they actually set up their image, they speak their line/phrase together from their seats. After this introduction, they should move slowly and deliberately into position. This will help them appreciate that they need to focus and concentrate as soon as they move from their seats, not just when they 'freeze' their image.

✳ Suggest to the children who are watching that they take on the role of Hamelin's townspeople who are being reminded of the effects that the rats are having on their comfortable lives. After the images have been seen, ask the townspeople how they feel about what is going on and what they intend to do about it.

Lesson Three
Listening and responding
(watching others' presentations)

In this lesson the teacher tells the story of and reads part of the poem 'The Pied Piper of Hamelin' to the children, pausing to ask their opinion of the characters involved and culminating in a discussion on what part of the performance they enjoyed or did not enjoy.

Intended learning
- To describe what the characters are like.

Whole class

✻ Read the poem to the children using an illustrated version that you can show to them as you read. There is a cartoon version on photocopiable Sheet Eight (page 47) which you could display on an OHP or whiteboard and the children could follow as you read.

✻ Tell the children that the people flocked to the town hall to demand that the corporation (a bit like our town councils today) do something about all the rats. As the corporation was debating the problem there was a tapping at the door. In came the pied piper, who told them he could get rid of the rats for them for one thousand guilders. They agreed and the pied piper stepped out into the street and blew on his pipe 'three shrill notes'.

✻ To the accompaniment of the music by Debussy, read as much of the next stanza as possible as the children will love it:

'And the muttering grew to a grumbling;
And the grumbling grew to a mighty rumbling;
And out of the houses the rats came tumbling.
Great rats, small rats, lean rats, brawny rats...'

✻ And so the piper led the rats away from the town and into the Weser river.

✻ Tell the children (or read it to them – stanza 8) that the piper asked for his thousand guilders and the mayor refused to pay. He thought that because the rats were dead there would be nothing the pied piper could do about it.

✻ Read stanza 12 in which the piper plays his pipe and all the children come running. Either read the rest of the story or tell it, showing the pictures from the book or referring them to the version you have displayed, until the children disappear into the side of the mountain – all except for one poor child who was lame and couldn't keep up.

Groups

✻ Organise the children into groups to discuss both the behaviour of the mayor and the pied piper. Was the mayor wrong to refuse to pay the piper? Was the pied piper wrong to steal the children away?

Plenary

✻ Ask the groups to report back to the whole class their thoughts on the behaviour of the mayor and the pied piper. These could be recorded on the board and the class take votes on which they agree with and which they disagree with.

✻ Ask the children to tell you what they liked about the story poem. Was there anything they didn't like? Discuss any difficult words they may have heard. Use a class dictionary to find out their meanings.

✻ What do the children think of the characters in the story? Ask individuals to tell you.

Lesson Four
Speaking for different audiences
(telling real and imagined stories)

In this lesson the children will consider the different points of view of some of the characters in the poem, then be organised into groups in order to plan how the different characters would tell their stories to different audiences. The lesson culminates in a story-telling session.

Intended learning
- To include relevant detail.
- To use the conventions of storytelling.
- To keep the listeners' interest.
- To sustain an account.

Whole class
✳ Talk to the children about the different characters in the poem: the mayor, the councillors, the pied piper, the people and the children. How do they think these different people felt about what happened?

✳ Discuss the mayor:
- Why did he act as he did?
- Was he keeping the money for himself?
- Was the town too poor to pay the money?
- Did he realise what would happen to the town if he did not pay the money?
- Was he a good person or a bad person?

✳ Discuss the pied piper:
- Where did he come from?
- Why did he want the money?
- How did he learn how to play the pipe in such a special way?
- Why did he lead the children away?
- Was he a good person or a bad person?

✳ Talk about the children:
- How did they feel about the rats?
- Did they enjoy living in Hamelin?
- What did they think when the piper came?
- What did they think when the piper got rid of the rats?
- Why did they follow him when they heard his music?

✳ Finally, talk about the parents:
- How did they feel about the rats?
- Did they enjoy living in Hamelin?
- What did they think when the piper came?
- What did they think when the piper got rid of the rats?
- What did they think when the mayor wouldn't pay the piper?
- How did they feel when the piper took the children away?

Groups

✳ Tell the children they are now going to work in groups to plan how the different characters might tell their version of the story. Explain that each character is to tell his or her story to a different audience:

- The mayor will tell his story to the crowd, explaining why he did what he did.

- The pied piper will tell his story to the mayor, explaining why he did what he did.

- A parent will tell his or her story to another parent, explaining what happened as they saw it and what should happen next.

- A child will tell his or her story to the audience.

✳ You may like to have two other groups, one to represent the story from the rats' point of view and the other to re-enact the story from the point of view of the lame child who didn't make it into the mountain with the others.

✳ Help the children with the ways in which they will need to speak.

- The mayor speaking to the people would be whining and apologetic, saying things like 'I didn't mean it. I didn't think he would do that. I'll do anything to make it up to you.' He wants to keep his job!

- The piper will be angry in the way he tells his story to the mayor: 'I came all this way to help you and what did you do?' and 'It's your fault the children have gone!'

- The parent will be feeling sorry for him/herself as well as angry with the mayor: 'My lovely daughter and your handsome son were taken away. What shall we do? It's all the mayor's fault!'

- The child, who is talking to the audience, could have many different approaches. Perhaps the place they went to was much better than Hamelin. But does he or she miss his or her mother and father? Are all the children still together? Do they like the pied piper or not?

✳ Let the groups spend some time planning who is going to do the talking and what they are going to say.

Plenary

✳ Ask each of the groups to present their speech to the other groups. Remind them that they are not speaking as if to the other children in the class but as if to the person they have been told they are speaking to.

✳ When everyone has had their turn, talk about the speeches. Does everyone agree with what was said? Do some children have different points of view? For example, does anyone think the mayor is a kind man or the pied piper a bad man?

Looking after pets

Overall aims

- To study the responsibilities involved in keeping pets.
- To identify and ask relevant questions and research answers.
- To prepare and organise the researched material for presentation to others.

Resources

- RSPCA or PDSA spokesperson or vet.
- A1 paper for display purposes.
- An empty water bottle for a rabbit.
- Books and Internet articles on keeping pets.

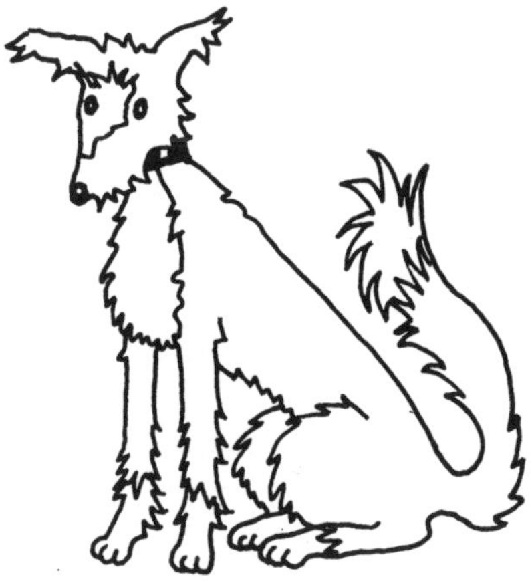

In this lesson the children will discuss different types of pets and their needs, then work in groups to draw up questions to put to an expert in relation to those pets and needs.

Lesson One
Listening and responding
(to a talk by an adult)

Intended learning

- To remember specific points.
- To respond to others' reactions.
- To identify what they learned.

Notes for the teacher

Studying how to behave responsibly towards other creatures, and knowledge of the organisations and services that support this undertaking are elements of PSHE/citizenship. The science curriculum at Key Stage 1 also includes the study of animals and their needs.

Invite a guest speaker from the RSPCA or PDSA, or a vet, to attend this lesson and deliver a question and answer session at the end of it. It is important that it is agreed by everyone, including the class, that the guest is there to observe and listen at first rather than lead or even take part in the preliminary discussion. The guest's expertise will be called on when the children have identified the questions they want answered.

Whole class

- To establish what the children already know about caring for pet animals, start by asking who in the class keeps any pets – animals, birds, fish. Record on the board a list of the species the children own. If this produces a sufficiently varied sample (more than simply dogs and cats), it may not be necessary to ask for more. If yours is not a pet-owning class, however, expand the list a little by including the pets of people the children know – friends, neighbours or relatives. The object is to keep within a range of pets that reflects the children's experience and knowledge and to include some diversity. (It is hoped, however, that none of the children own anything as unusual as a crocodile!)

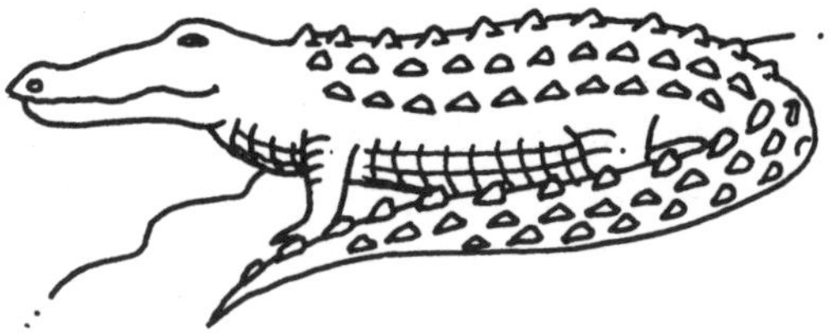

✳ In order to identify the key questions that arise if one is to treat pet creatures responsibly, discuss with the children what different pets require if they are to live safely, happily and in good health. Start to identify categories of requirement, for example a suitable habitat, sustenance, hygiene, exercise, playthings and company (human and animal) – by recording the children's responses in appropriate clusters on the board. When clear examples of these categories have emerged, help the children to identify them as categories by asking them, for example, for a word for where animals sleep and live and where they run, swim or fly.

✳ At this stage, you are still trying to establish what the children already know and what it is they might need to discover rather than trying to teach them anything new, but it might be useful to introduce terms such as habitat, environment or territory, if some of the children are not yet familiar with them. However, 'where they live' would be a perfectly good alternative, as would 'food and drink', 'keeping clean' and 'animal toys'.

✳ Keep the list of categories (although not necessarily the items in each category) either on the board or on a display sheet on the classroom wall.

Groups

✳ Ask the children to work in groups to draw up a list of questions they would like answered under the various category headings. You, your classroom assistants and your guest speaker might like to help the children with this task. The questions should be the children's but they might include such things as:

- Can you overfeed an animal?

- What dangers can arise with regard to feeding (for example, chicken bones are not for dogs, nor peanuts for rabbits)? Why?

- Are some animals happier by themselves? Which different species of animal live happily together?

- Do most pets like being held and stroked? Can you train a pet to like it if it seems uneasy at first?

- What are the best ways of holding various creatures?

- Is it cruel to keep a rabbit or a hamster locked up in a hutch all the time? What are the possible alternatives?

- Do different breeds of dog need different amounts of exercise?

Plenary

✳ Let the children ask their questions. After a period of questions and answers, ask the class to identify the most important things they have learned both from your guest speaker and from each other.

✳ Time permitting, some whole class feedback on what they have just discussed would be appropriate. What specific points do they remember? What are their knowledge and concerns?

Lesson Two
Drama activities
(performance)

In this lesson, the children will have the opportunity to tell stories in role as pets. They are required to sustain their role and create dramatic incidents as the victims of inconsiderate human behaviour.

Intended learning

- To present their own story to peers.
- To sustain work in role.
- To create dramatic incidents.

Whole class

✢ Gather the class around you. Signal that you have something secret to convey but say as little as possible until the children are settled. When they are ready, brandish a rabbit's empty feeding bottle for everyone to see. You are representing a very thirsty pet rabbit and you are about to address the class as a secret, night-time gathering of pet animals.

✢ In as croaky a voice as you can manage, say something like:

'I'm glad you have all made it. Did any of you have difficulties escaping from your cages, kennels, hutches?' To one, whom you are now identifying as a cat, say 'It would be easy for you, of course. You just curl up at the foot of your human's bed, don't you? I hope you didn't wake him when you jumped down! We'll have to be very quiet so as not to wake any of them now. I've called this meeting because I can't stand it any longer.' Shake the empty bottle, turning it upside down to stress the point. 'Look at this. Empty. And it's been empty for two days now. I can hardly talk I'm so dry. They don't know how to look after us, do they?' Pointing to a child and pretending he or she is a pet dog, say 'I know you haven't been for a proper walk for weeks, have you? What about the rest of you? What problems are you having?'

✢ If the children have read your signals correctly, they will start to offer examples of how their humans have been neglecting or even ill-treating them. Let this go on until most have entered into the fiction and are playing the game of being long-suffering pets. When you feel that this fiction is well established, or if you sense it is not established at all, come out of role and ask everyone to choose what different species they would like to represent.

✢ Reconvene the secret meeting of animals and say something like, 'Now I know we don't all know each other so I suggest we get together in animal groups and agree what, for each of us, the main problem with our owner is. Then we'll decide what is to be done.'

Groups

✢ Form the children into groups of the same or similar species and ask them to identify their needs. What do the humans have to do to satisfy their needs? You may need to jog the children's memories of what they identified under the various categories, which will still be on display from the previous lesson.

✢ Ask each group to devise one incident where an animal, fish or bird has come up against inconsiderate human behaviour. The group may simply agree on what the incident is or they may act out the incident with members of the group adopting the roles of humans and pets.

Plenary

✢ Reconvene the secret meeting and invite each group to tell or demonstrate its chosen incident. Respond by saying that this situation is dreadful and something needs to be done about it. Allow the children to make suggestions. (If simply running away is proposed, remind them that they are not equipped to live in the wild. They are pets. They wouldn't survive on their own.)

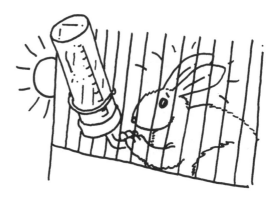

Lesson Three
Discussion and group interaction
(explaining, reporting, evaluating)

In this lesson the fiction that you and the children are badly cared for pets is continued. They consider a contract to be drawn up between pet and owner, work in groups to plan and draft the contract and then present the final version to the class for discussion prior to presenting it to the owners.

Intended learning

- To ensure each group member takes a turn.
- To organise helpful links between contributions when reporting.
- To review how the group tackled the task and worked together.

Whole class

❋ Recall the fictional situation with the animals in the last lesson and ask the children how they are going to get the humans to look after them (the pets) properly.

❋ After considering the feasibility of whatever is proposed, suggest that the children draw up contracts for humans that will include these proposals, and develop them. As a class, consider what such a contract might look like. You can suggest that it might start something like this:

We, the undersigned, being responsible for the health, welfare and happiness of our pet animals, fish, birds, agree that it is our duty to undertake the following tasks:

And will conclude with:

Signed _____

Date _____

Groups

❋ In their groups from Lesson Two, ask the children to work on a contract for their human carers, listing all the duties and responsibilities to which their pet owner must agree. Stress the importance of each member of the group contributing to this document. Each group should concentrate on the particular needs of the pets they represent.

❋ At this point, indicate the books and Internet articles about looking after animals that are available for the children to consult.

❋ Ask the children to use ICT to create the contracts in a suitable format. As well as being instruction booklets on how to look after particular pets, the contracts might include plans of an animal dwelling (suitably labelled), appropriate pet menus, games to be played with one's pet, exercise routines, how to handle or hold various creatures. Once again, the children are identifying and consolidating what they have learned.

Plenary

❋ Invite each group to present their contract to the whole class. They could redraft it in the light of any feedback. In compiling their final drafts, ask the children to look for the ideas that fall into the categories identified in Lesson One and attempt to organise them in an orderly way. Which ideas follow on from each other? Which are linked by a common theme?

❋ Invite the class to reflect on how successful they consider their drawing up of each contract has been. Ask the children to consider whether they have included everything they need to. Have they listened to everyone's ideas? Do they think that the humans will be convinced that they should undertake to behave as required?

Lesson Four
Speaking for different audiences
(presentation: explaining processes or information)

In this final lesson the children practise in their groups the delivery of the final versions of the contracts they have drawn up to the owners. They prepare in the groups for any questions that might be asked and then make the final formal presentation.

Intended learning

- To ensure items are clearly sequenced.
- To use selected, relevant detail.
- To end accounts effectively.

Whole class

❋ Tell the children that they are now going to present their contracts for animal carers to the humans. As they will be reading a formal document, their reading style should not be chatty but serious.

❋ Ask them to return to their groups to practise the reading and to prepare for any questions that the owners might ask them.

❋ You could choose one of the groups, ask them to do a rehearsal of their presentations and, using it as an example, help the children to sequence some of the questions there might be about it under the categories identified in Lesson One. For example, to do with feeding, then exercise and so on.

Groups

❋ Let the groups decide who will make the presentation. They may wish to share it between them. They should then practise speaking out loud. It might be an idea to let the groups work in different places within the school bounds, so that their public speaking does not interfere with others. Ask the groups to look at the questions they might be asked, sequence them under the agreed categories and plan their answers to them.

❋ Encourage the children to select relevant detail in answering the questions. For example, if a dog's coat is being brushed, in which direction should the brush strokes be made? And what do you need in order to give a dog a bath – hot water, cold water, soap or shampoo?

❋ Explain to the children how they might end their answer by checking with 'the humans' that their question has been satisfactorily answered.

The presentation

❋ In turn, ask one member of each group to introduce the presentation and then read the contract to the rest of the class (or a neighbouring class). The other members of the group can then explain the detail and answer any questions that might arise when the reading is over.

Plenary

❋ As a class, discuss the effectiveness of each presentation. Have the humans been convinced that they should sign the contracts and agree to the pets' demands? Gather the pets together again and congratulate them on their achievements.

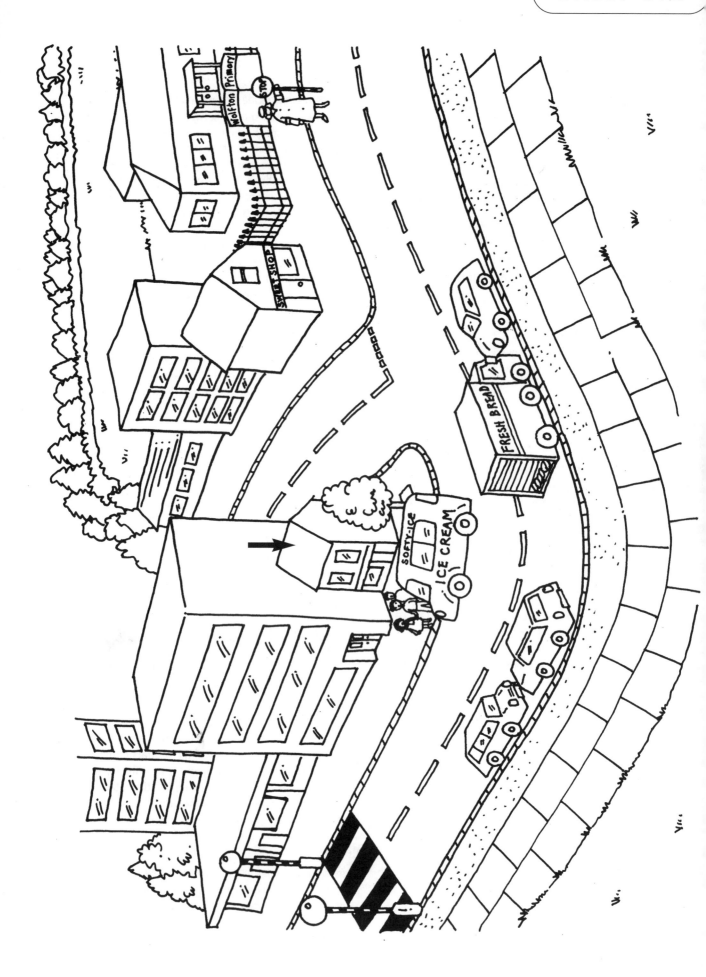

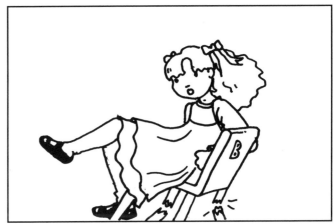

Name _____

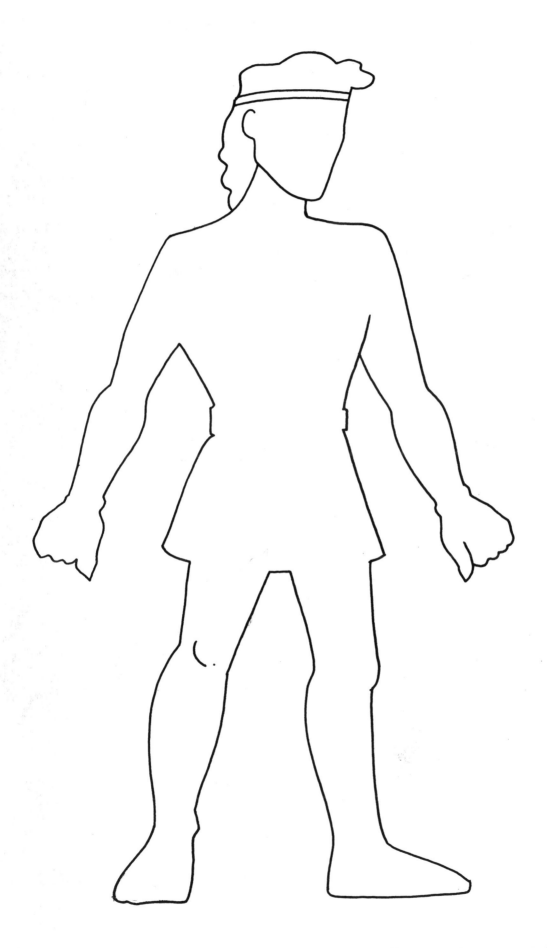

Hercules is the son of the god Zeus, who lives on Mount Olympus in Greece, and a mortal woman.

Hades, the god of the underworld where the dead go, wants to get rid of Zeus and live on Mount Olympus himself. The Fates – three horrid females! – tell him that he will succeed in a few years' time but only if Hercules is no longer a god. So Hades has the baby Hercules captured and given a potion that will make him a mortal! But his plan goes wrong and Hercules, although no longer a god, still keeps his incredible strength.

Hercules is found by a childless couple who bring him up. He is a kind child who is very strong and very clumsy! But he knows that he is no ordinary person, so one day he goes to the temple of Zeus to ask his advice. The statue of Zeus comes to life and tells Hercules that he is his father. He tells Hercules what happened and how he can become a god again – he has to do something incredibly brave.

Hercules seeks the help of Philoctetes, a satyr who helps people become heroes. One day, while he is training as a hero, Hercules rescues a young woman, Meg, from a centaur, a creature half man and half horse. Then he becomes a hero by slaying the many-headed hydra. The people all love him and shout 'You're a hero!'

Hercules goes on to perform twelve labours, saving the people of Thebes from the many terrors that surround them.

The people build a statue of him, print his picture on vases, make action toys of him and much more. So, Hercules goes again to his father Zeus and asks to become a god again because of his achievements, but Zeus says he has not shown true bravery yet.

Then Hercules meets Meg again and, not knowing she is in the power of Hades, falls in love with her. And she falls in love with him.

Hades now plans again to finish Hercules off, so that he can defeat Zeus. He holds Meg hostage and tells Hercules he will release her from his power if Hercules promises to lose all his strength for one day. Hercules agrees and Hades sets off to defeat Zeus. He sets free the mighty Titans, including the one-eyed cyclops, which he sends to kill Hercules!

Zeus fights a mighty battle with the Titans and Hercules fights and finally defeats the cyclops, using just bravery as he has no strength left. But during the fight Meg is accidentally killed! Hercules is determined to save her and he goes to the underworld to rescue her. The underworld is a terrifying place, full of the dead! But Hercules is brave again and he manages to bring Meg back into the real world and back to life.

Because of his true bravery Zeus tells him he has become a god again.

But Hercules chooses to remain a mortal so that he can be with his Meg.

Storytelling: All Join In!

Aim:	Prior Learning:	Resources:
Recognising and joining in with predictable phrases. Learning to appreciate rhymes and poems, and to recite some by heart. I can learn the story off by heart and perform it.	None needed.	Lesson Pack Large paper Pens Chalks Percussion instruments 'We're Going on a Bear Hunt' by Michael Rosen
Success Criteria: I can join in with the repeating parts of the story. I can retell the story out loud. I can use sound effects and drama to make my performance more interesting.	**Key/New Words:** Performance, perform.	**Preparation:** Story Sequencing Cards as required Bear Hunt Word Mat as required Reading Aloud Marking Checklist per pair Bear Hunt Story Map Activity Sheet as required

Learning Sequence

	Read It! Read the text with the children. Identify the repeating parts and encourage them to join in with them. Can the children join in with predictable phrases?	
	Do It! In pairs, children devise physical actions for the predictable phrases of the story which they have already identified. Read the story again as a whole class, with the children adding their actions. Split the class in half and children take it in turns to retell the story, showing their actions to the other group. Children give verbal feedback – one positive comment and one improvement suggestion. Can the children add drama to their performance?	
	Order It! Children sequence the **Story Sequencing Cards** with their partner and match to the relevant sound button the **Lesson Presentation**. On large pieces of paper (or outside with chalks), children draw a story map with the obstacles in the correct order. Label each with the description and sound effects used in the original text. Use the **Bear Hunt Story Map Activity Sheet** if more appropriate. Children select percussion instruments or body percussion to add sound effects for each one. In pairs, practise retelling the story with the actions and sound effects chosen. Can the children add sound effects to their performance?	
	Perform It! Show the **Reading Aloud Marking Checklist** on the **Lesson Presentation**. Add 'Use drama and sound effects?' in the Structure and Language section. Children to take it in turns, in groups of 4, to show each other their performance. Use the **Bear Hunt Word Mats** and their story maps for help. Children mark their friend's retelling, using the **Reading Aloud Marking Checklist**. (You may wish to add 'Use drama and sound effects?' to the children's version or get them to do so.) Can the children retell the story using drama and sound effects, and use a checklist to mark each other's work?	

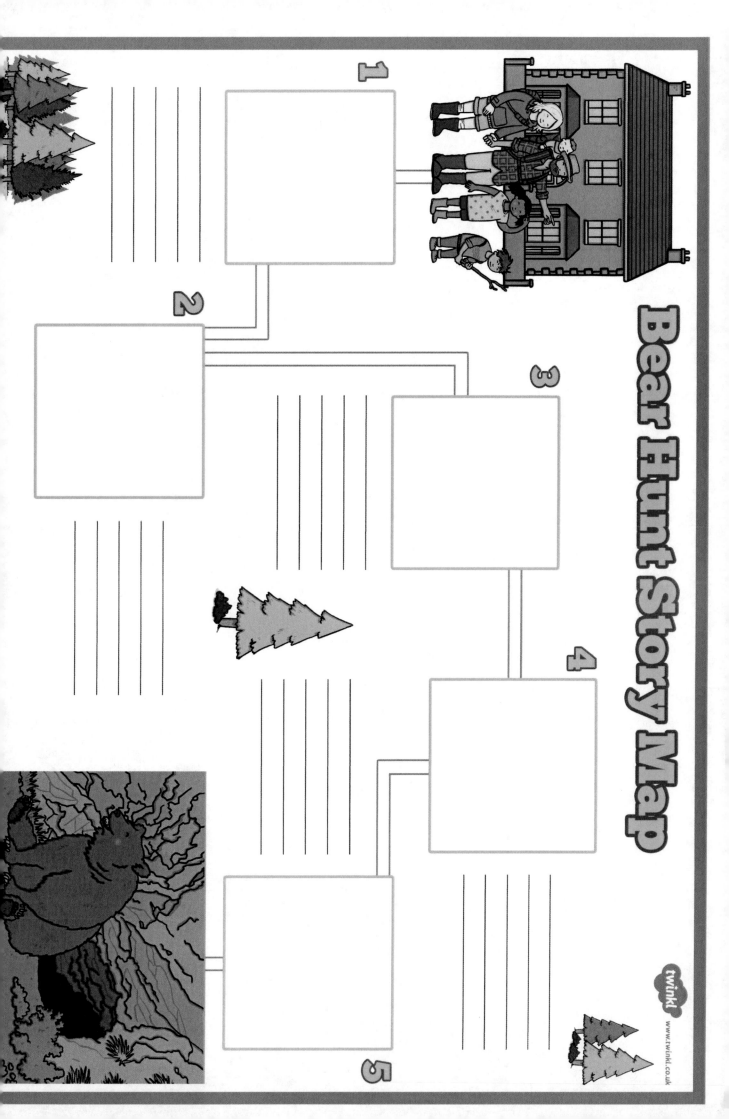

Bear Hunt Story Map

1

2

3

4

5

Animal Hunt Story Map

I can use what I know about 'We're Going on a Bear Hunt' by Michael Rosen, to plan my own story with repeating parts.

Draw and describe the obstacles you will meet on your animal hunt, in the boxes. Write the adjectives to describe the sound effects you will make as you go through it, on the lines underneath. Draw your last illustration to show what the animal does after the letter has been delivered.

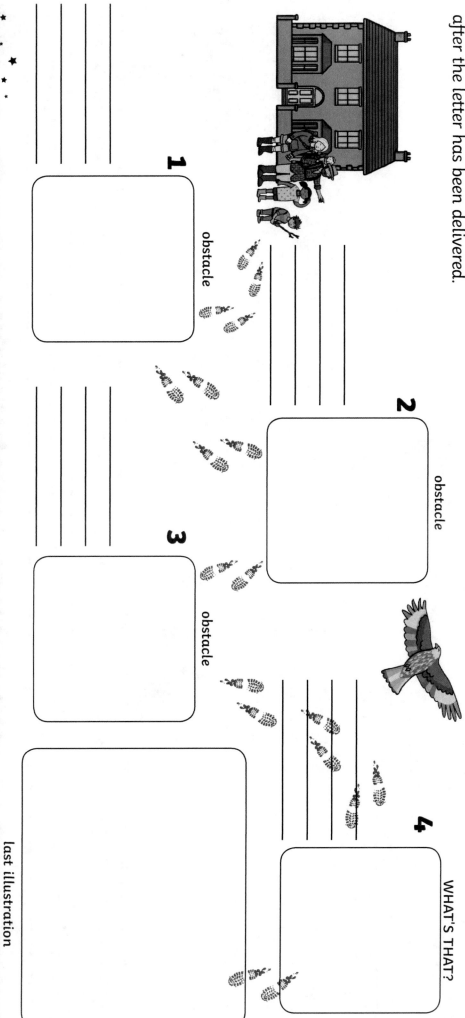

1

obstacle

2

obstacle

3

obstacle

4

WHAT'S THAT?

last illustration

Animal Hunt Story Map

I can use what I know about 'We're Going on a Bear Hunt' by Michael Rosen, to plan my own story with repeating parts.

Draw and describe the obstacles you will meet on your animal hunt, in the boxes. Write the adjectives to describe the sound effects you will make as you go through it, on the lines underneath. Draw your last illustration to show what the animal does after the letter has been delivered.

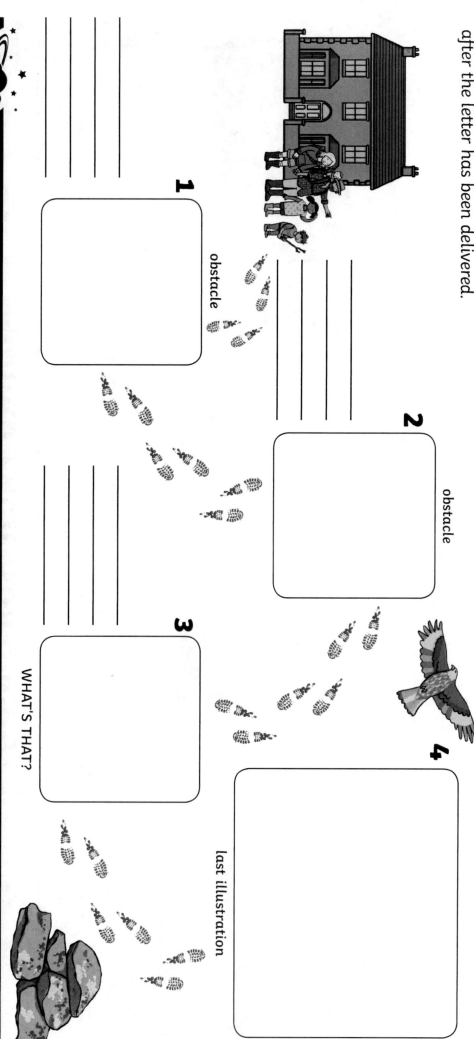

obstacle

1

2

obstacle

3

WHAT'S THAT?

4

last illustration

Animal Hunt Story Map

I can use what I know about 'We're Going on a Bear Hunt' by Michael Rosen, to plan my own story with repeating parts.

Draw and describe the obstacles you will meet on your animal hunt, in the boxes. Write the adjectives to describe the sound effects you will make as you go through it, on the lines underneath. Draw your last illustration to show what the animal does after the letter has been delivered.

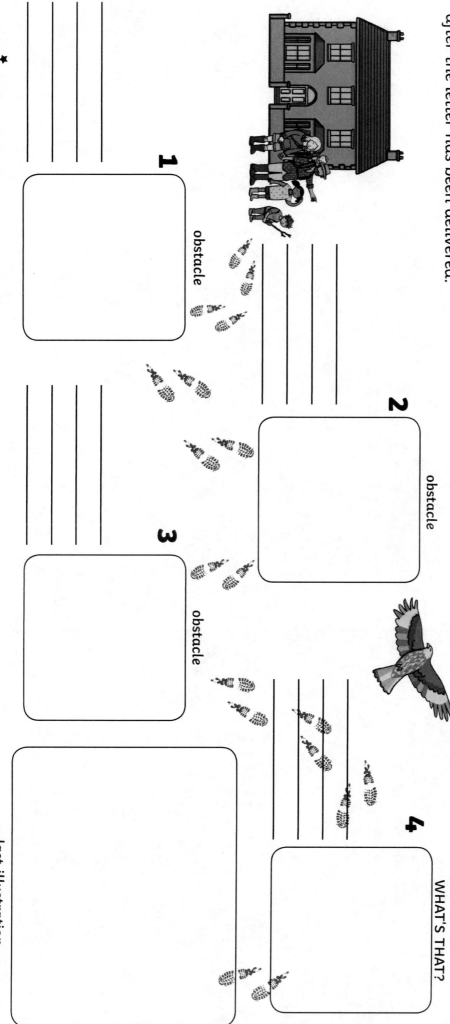

1

obstacle

2

obstacle

3

obstacle

4

WHAT'S THAT?

last illustration